The children put some tables outside.

1

They wanted to help
Children in Need.

Chip made a poster. It said,
"Help Children in Need".

Biff and Nadim had some plants.

Kipper and Wilma had some
clothes. Wilf had some books.

Anneena had a good idea. She
invented a game.

Dad looked at Anneena's game.
"Let me have a go," he said.

A man put Dad's jacket on.
"It's a good fit," he said.

"It's five pounds," said Wilma.
The man bought the jacket.

Dad looked for his jacket.

"Oh no!" said Wilma. "I'm
sorry. A man bought it."

Dad ran after the man.
"Stop!" he called. "That's my jacket."

"No, it's my jacket," said the man.
"Give me ten pounds for it."

"Oh no," said Dad. He gave the
man ten pounds.

The man gave the jacket to Dad.

The man gave Wilma ten pounds.
"It's for Children in Need," he said.